TAKING TIME

SENIOR AUTHORS

Virginia A. Arnold   **Carl B. Smith**

AUTHORS

James Flood   **Diane Lapp**

LITERATURE CONSULTANTS

Joan I. Glazer   Margaret H. Lippert

Macmillan Publishing Company
New York

Collier Macmillan Publishers
London

ACKNOWLEDGMENTS

The publisher gratefully acknowledges permission to reprint the following copyrighted material:

"At the edge of the world" from SINGING FOR POWER, Ruth Murray Underhill, editor. © 1938 Ruth Murray Underhill. Used by permission of the University of California Press.

"Change" from RIVER WINDING by Charlotte Zolotow (Thomas Y. Crowell). Text copyright © 1970 by Charlotte Zolotow. Reprinted by permission of Harper & Row, Publishers, Inc. and World's Work Ltd.

"Darlene" is excerpted from DARLENE by Eloise Greenfield. Copyright © 1980 by Eloise Greenfield. Illustrations by George Ford. Copyright © 1980 by George Ford. Published by Methuen, Inc., 29 West 35 Street, N.Y. 10001.

"A Desert Animal" and pictures from "A Desert Animal" by Jeff Hall. Reprinted by permission of the author.

"The Guest" with selected illustrations from OWL AT HOME by Arnold Lobel. Copyright © 1975 by Arnold Lobel. Reprinted by permission of Harper & Row, Publishers, Inc. and World's Work Ltd.

"Hello and Good-By" from HELLO AND GOOD-BY by Mary Anne Hoberman. Copyright © 1959 by Mary Ann Hoberman. Reprinted by permission of Russell & Volkening, Inc. as agents for the author.

"Leo the Late Bloomer" is the entire text, verbatim and ten specified illustrations from LEO THE LATE BLOOMER by Robert Kraus. Pictures by José Aruego (Windmill Books/Thomas Y. Crowell Co.). Text copyright © 1971 by Robert Kraus. Illustrations copyright © 1971 by José Aruego. By permission of Windmill Books, Inc. and Harper & Row, Publishers, Inc. By permission also of Hamish Hamilton, Ltd.

"Night Comes" from A BUNCH OF POEMS AND VERSES by Beatrice Schenk de Regniers. Text copyright © 1977 by Beatrice Schenk de Regniers. Reprinted by permission of Ticknor & Fields/ Clarion Books, a Houghton Mifflin Company.

Cover Design: Josie Yee   **Unit Openers:** Bob Shein

Feature Logos and Medallion Logos: Eva Vagreti Cockrille

ILLUSTRATION CREDITS: Sal Murdocca, 4–8; Jan Palmer, 10–15; Lynn Breeze, 16–23; Laurie Jordan, 24–25; Morissa Lipstein, 26–27, 66–67, 84–85, 130–131, 148–149, 166–167; John Sanford, 28–37; Jan Pyk, 39, 185; Hima Pamoedjo, 40–47; Jerry Smath, 48–57; Anik Lafreniere, 58–65; Lulu Delacre, 74–83; Ed Parker, 86–93; Barbara Lanza, 94–95; George Ford, 96–103; Ken Longtemps, 106–115; Jan Sterret, 116–117; Phillipe Beha, 118–129; Terry Burton, 132–141; June Otoni Baensh, 142–147; Gay Holland, 150–159; Mireille Levert, 160–161; Jeff Hall, 162–165; Jon Fraser, 168–173; José Aruego, 174–183; Arnold Lobel, 186–199; Maureen Galvani, 201–220; John Nez, 226–240.

PHOTO CREDITS: © Lizzy Rockwell, 34; © Ken Lax, 40–47, 68–73; Photo Researchers, Inc.: © Scott Camazine, 164; © Courtesy of the author, 184.

Contents

Introducing Level 4

NEW FRIENDS

In this unit, you will read about the things friends do together. How do you and your friends have fun together?

"It isn't much fun for One,
but Two can stick together,"
says Pooh, says he.

A. A. Milne

9

A New Friend

Marjorie Weinman Sharmat

A new friend can show you what you
do not know.
You can show a new friend what you
know, too.

Betty was up with the sun.

She ran to see Mother.

"Get up, Mother," Betty said.

"You said we could go to the gym."

"Was that what I said?" Mother said.

"It was," said Betty.

"We will take the bus," said Mother.

"Look at that little girl,"
said Betty.

"You look sad, Betty," said Mother.
"What is it?"

Betty said, "I wish a little girl
like that was my friend."

At the gym, Betty said to Mother,
"Look, that is the girl on the bus.
Look at what she can do on the mat!"

"Go to the mat," said Mother.
"She may help you."

Betty ran to the new girl.
She said, "I like what you can do
on the mat."

The new girl said, "I can't jump
like you can."

Betty said, "I could help you jump,
and you could help me on the mat."

13

Mother said, "Betty, it is time to
go home."
Betty ran, but the new girl ran, too.
Betty said, "My name is Betty."

The new girl said, "My name is Betty!
A new friend, and with my name, too.
What do you know!"

"I know a new friend with my name,"
said Betty.
"That is what I know!"

Thinking and Writing About the Selection

1. What will the new girl help Betty do?

2. What will Betty help the new girl do?

3. What can you show a new friend?

THE GIANT

Jim Razzi

Mike and Greg like to play at night.
Read to see what they will do.

It is night, and the moon is out.
Mike says, "I like to look
at the moon."

Greg says, "I don't like to sit and
look at the moon.
I like to run.
Will you play tag with me?"

"Not now, Greg," says Mike.

"Look!" says Greg.
"The moon is not out.
Can we play tag now?"

"Not now, Greg," says Mike.
"Now I can see the stars."

"I will get mad at you," says Greg.

"Go on and get mad," says Mike.

"You are not fun, Mike," says Greg.
"You will not run with me.
You will not play tag with me in
the night.
You don't like to play at night.
You are not brave!"

18

Mike looks at the stars.
"I like to look up stars in my book," he says.

Greg says, "Mike is not brave, but look at me!
I like to run and play in the night!"
He stops quickly.
"Look, Mike!" he says.
"What is that?"

"I don't know," says Mike.

"It is a giant!" says Greg.
"Run!"

Mike looks and looks.
Is it a giant?

"Quickly!" says Greg.
"Run!
The giant will get us!"

"Don't run," says Mike.
"That giant can't get us."

"Yes, it can!
Yes, it can!" says Greg.
"Giants are big.
They can run quickly!"

"This giant can't get us," says Mike.
"Now the moon is out.
Look!"

"I see," says Greg.
"It is not a giant.
You know, Mike, you are brave,
not me."

"I know where giants are," says Mike.

"Where are they?" says Greg.

"They are in books," says Mike.

"Can we get a book on giants?"
says Greg.

"Yes, we can," says Mike,
"but now we will play tag!
You are it!"

Thinking and Writing About the Selection

1. What did Mike like to do?

2. What did Greg like to do?

3. What is the giant?

Night Comes

Night comes
leaking
out of the sky.

Stars come
peeking.

Moon comes
sneaking,
silvery-sly.

Who is
shaking,
shivery-
quaking?

Who is afraid
of the night?

Not I.

*Beatrice Schenk
de Regniers*

25

SEQUENCE OF EVENTS

Here is what two boys do one night.

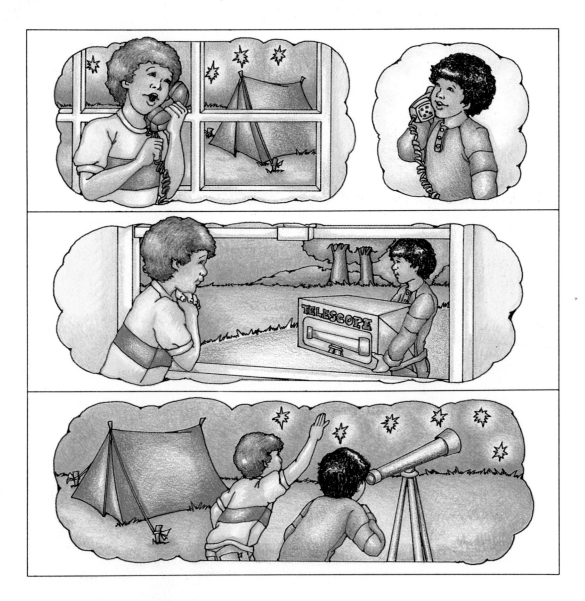

Read the sentences.

They say what the boys did.

> • Ben watches for Dan.
>
> • Dan and Ben go out to see the stars.
>
> • Dan says he can come to see Ben.

1. On your paper, write the sentence that says what Dan did first.
2. Write the sentence that says what Ben did next.
3. Then write the sentence that says what the boys did last.

Buster and the Fish

Anne Rockwell

Grandmother likes fish for pets.
Linda and Grandmother play with
the fish.
Will Buster play with the fish, too?

"Who is this?" asked Grandmother.

"It is Linda, Grandmother.
May Buster and I come to see you?"

"Yes, you may," said Grandmother.
"I will show you my new fish."

Linda and Buster came to
see Grandmother.
"Where is your new fish,
Grandmother?" asked Linda.
"May I see it now?"

"It is a very little one,"
said Grandmother.
"It is in my aquarium.
Come and see."

30

"I see your big fish, but I don't
see your new little one," said Linda.
"Where is it?"

"Look at the plants," said Grandmother.

"Now I see it," said Linda.
"I see the new fish in with the plants.
I can see six fish.
They look the same, but that one is
very little."

"May I feed your fish?" asked Linda.

"Yes," said Grandmother.
"You may feed the fish."

Buster came up to look.
"Down, Buster!" said Linda.
"Don't jump on the aquarium."
Buster sat down.

"Will the new little fish grow?"
asked Linda.

"Yes," said Grandmother.
"We will feed it, and it will
grow quickly."
Then Grandmother said,
"Look at Buster!"

"Buster!" said Linda.
"Don't do that!
Don't drink the aquarium water.
I will get water for you."

"An aquarium is for fish,
not a dog," said Grandmother.
"Come on, Buster, now we will go
out and play with you."

34

"Who will get the bag?" asked Linda.
Buster did.

"Now who will get it?"
asked Grandmother.
Buster did.
Buster ran up and down
and up and down.

Grandmother, Linda, and Buster
came in.
They sat down to drink water.
"I like to drink water," said Linda.

"I see that Buster likes to drink
water, too," said Grandmother.

"I like to see your fish swim in
the aquarium," said Linda, "but
they can't sit and drink with us.
They can't play with us like Buster can."

"Yes," said Grandmother.

"I like my pets.

Fish are fun to look at, but I

like your pet, too.

He is fun to play with!"

Thinking and Writing About the Selection

1. Where did Buster and Linda go?

2. What was in the aquarium?

 3. What pets do you like?

Anne Rockwell

When Anne Rockwell was a child, she couldn't decide whether to be an artist or a writer. She loved to draw and paint. Once she decorated her room with scenes from her favorite picture book. As she got older she developed a love for books. She says, "My closest friends were characters in books."

When Rockwell grew up, she became an artist. Later, she realized that she really wanted to make children's books. She got many ideas from her children and their friends.

More to Read   *First Comes Spring*
Our Garage Sale

NAME THAT FISH!

Here are fish that Grandmother could have in her aquarium.

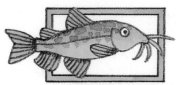
Catfish

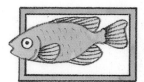
Neon fish

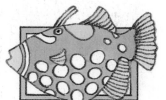
Triggerfish

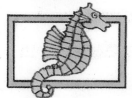
Sea Horse

Angler fish

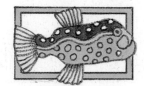
Box fish

What fish do you like?

On your paper, write the answer to the question.

1. What fish looks like a box?
2. How did the Neon fish get its name?
3. What fish looks like a cat?
4. What fish looks like a pony?
5. What fish looks like a plant?

AT THE AQUARIUM

Virginia A. Arnold

You can get a little aquarium
at home like Grandmother did.
You can go to a big aquarium
with Emily.
A big aquarium is like a water zoo
for fish.

My name is Emily.

My mother, my grandmother, and I are at an aquarium.

This aquarium isn't like my little one at home.

This aquarium is very big.

It is the home of big and little fish.

It is the home of seals and turtles, too.

First we look at the seals.

Then we pick up a map of the aquarium.

The map shows us all we can see
in the aquarium.

It shows us where we can see
more seals.

We can see sea lions!

Sea lions swim very quickly,
but they are not fish.

Sea lions are seals.

Now we can see a diver feed the fish.

The diver dives to where all the
fish are.

Now the fish see the diver.

They come quickly to feed.

More and more fish swim to the diver.

The diver dives to feed the
big turtles.
They live with the fish.
The turtles are very big, but
they can swim very quickly.

Next we walk down to see more of
the aquarium.
It looks like we are in the
water, too.
Isn't the water green?

Look at the sharks!
That one dives quickly down in
the water.
The sharks don't live with the
little fish.
Sharks feed on fish and plants.

At last we come out and sit
in the sun.
We look at the water.
Isn't it fun to go to the aquarium?
We all like it!
You will, too.

Thinking and Writing About the Selection

1. What shows Emily where to go
   in the aquarium?

2. What are sea lions?

3. What did the diver do?

New Friends for Catfish

Jerry Smath

Catfish, Seal, and Turtle all live
in the sea.
At first they are not all friends.
Read and see what they will do.

"Will you play with me?" Turtle
asked Seal.

"Yes," said Seal.
"I will play with you, Turtle.
That is what friends are for!"

"First we will play in the water,
and then we will sit in the sun,"
said Turtle.

Catfish came out to play.
"That looks like fun," he said.
"Will you let me play, too?"

"No, you may not," said Seal.
"We don't know you.
You look like a cat, but you are
a fish."

Turtle laughed.
"What are you?" he asked.

"I am a catfish, and I live on my own
boat," said Catfish.

"Where is your boat?" asked Seal.

"Let me play, and I will show it
to you," said Catfish.

"We will see," said Seal.
"First show us your boat."

"It is down in the water," said
Catfish.
"Come with me.
I will take you to see it.
We can all play in my boat."

Seal and Turtle came with Catfish
to the boat.

"This is my very own boat," said Catfish.
"Now may I play with you?"

In no time, Seal was in the boat.

"Come in and play," he said to Turtle.
"But you can't come in, Catfish.
You are no friend of mine!
Turtle is my friend.
We will play in this boat.
You may not!
Go and get your own boat!"

"But this boat *is* mine!" cried Catfish.
"You can't change that.
Let me come in and play
with you."

53

"No, you can't!" said Seal.
"This boat is mine now!
You may not come in!"
Seal and Turtle laughed at Catfish.

Catfish cried and cried.
"I will go and look for new
friends," he said.

"Come on in, Turtle," said Seal,
but Turtle could not get in.
Seal could not get out.
"Help!" cried Seal.
"Get me out!"

"Don't go, Catfish!" cried Turtle.
"Seal can't get out of your boat!"

Catfish did not go.
He came to help.
"I will push and push," he said.
"I will get you out."
Catfish did help.
Out came Seal at last.

"You came to help me, Catfish!"
said Seal.

"That is what friends are for,"
said Catfish.

"You *are* my friend," said Seal.
"I will change now.
I will not take what is not my own."

"I will change, too," said Turtle.
"I will not pick on you."
They all laughed.

"Come on," said Catfish.
"Let us all go and play in my boat."

Thinking and Writing About the Selection

1. Where did Catfish live?

2. What did Catfish do to help Seal?

3. How did Turtle and Seal change?

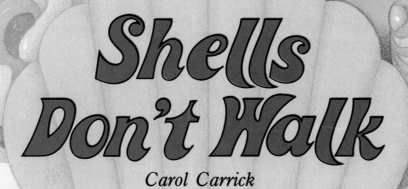

Shells Don't Walk

Carol Carrick

If you go to the sea, look for a
change in the water.
The tide will come in and go out.
Shells come in with the tide.

"This day is so pretty," said Jan.
"We can take a walk."

"Look at all the boats," said Tom.
"I like the red and green one."

"Look at all the shells," said Amy.
"They are so pretty.
May we take shells home with us?"

"Me too, me too!" said little Ben.
"May I take shells home, too?"

"All of us will look for shells," laughed Jan.
"I know things you can make with shells.
Find big shells and little shells."

Tom and Amy ran to see who could
find more shells.

"You come with me, Ben," said Jan.
"We will find shells, too."

Tom and Amy ran up to Jan and Ben.
"Look at all the pretty shells,"
they said.

"So I see," said Jan.
"Where can we put all of your things?"

"I can put my shells in this bag,"
said Tom.

Jan said, "This bag is for Amy and Ben.
I don't see a bag for my shells,
so I will put mine in my hat for now.
Now go look for bits of wood.
I will show you what to do with the
wood and the shells at home."

At last, it was time to go home.
"What will we do with the wood?"
asked Ben.

"You will see," said Jan.
"Now, where is my hat?" she asked.
"Where are my shells?
Tom, are they in your bag?"

"No," said Tom.
"I did not take your shells."

Jan asked Ben and Amy, "Did you
hide my shells?"

"No," they said.

Jan said, "Look, I had shells,
and I had a hat.
My hat was on that rock.
Shells don't walk, and my hat can't fly!
Did you play a trick on me?"

"We did not trick you," they said.

"We will all help you find your
shells and your hat, Jan," said Amy.

"Look, Jan!" Ben said.
"I see your hat in the water!"

"I see it, too!" cried Jan.
"The tide is in.
The water will take my things!"

"I will get your hat," said Tom.

"Now I see the trick," laughed Jan.
"Shells don't walk and a hat
can't fly.
But they can swim like mad if the
tide is in!"

Thinking and Writing About the Selection

1. Where did Amy and Tom put shells?

2. Where did the hat with the shells go?

3. What things could you make with shells
   and wood?

65

ANTONYMS

A. Look at the two sentences. Then look at the words that have a line under them.

The girl <u>laughed</u>.   The girl <u>cried</u>.

The words <u>cried</u> and <u>laughed</u> are **opposites**.

Find the word in a box that is the opposite of each word below. Write the two words on your paper.

up	day	no	go

1. yes <u>no</u>   2. night _____

3. stop _____   4. down _____

B. Look at the word with a line under it in each sentence.
Find the word in the box that is the opposite.
Write the sentences on your paper.

stop	little	out	down	last

1. Betty is the <u>first</u> one home.
   Greg is the <u>last</u> one home.

2. You can <u>go</u> on a green light.
   You have to _____ for a red light.

3. Watch the sea lion jump <u>up</u>.
   Watch when the turtle dives _____.

4. Amy has a <u>big</u> bag of shells.
   Tom has a _____ bag of shells.

5. The seals are <u>in</u> the water.
   Can the fish jump _____ of the aquarium?

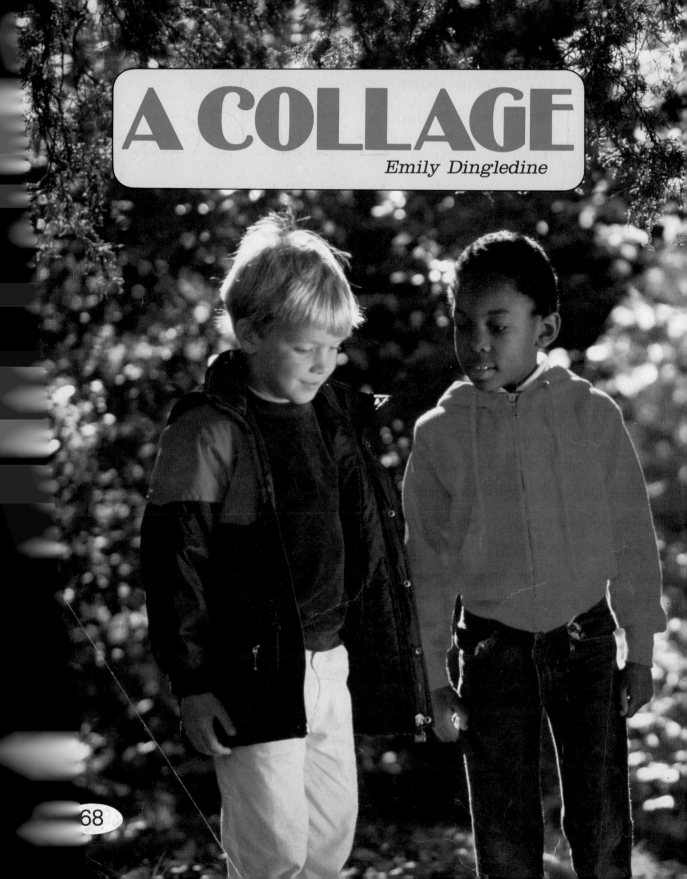

A COLLAGE

Emily Dingledine

*Jan, Amy, Ben, and Tom look
for shells and bits of wood
in the water.
You can find things in the
woods, too.*

You can make a pretty collage with
things that you can find on
the ground.
This is how you can do it.

First you need to walk in the woods
in the fall.
Look for seeds, pods, and nuts.
They are on the ground in the fall.

Then you will need to look for bits of wood on the ground.
Put the things you have in a bag.

Next, pick things that you like to put in your collage. How do you make a collage with your things?

You will need glue and wood to make your collage.

Glue the things you have on wood.

Your nuts, seeds, pods, and bits of wood make a collage on the wood.

Now you have a fall collage.

Thinking and Writing About the Selection

1. Where can you find things to make a pretty collage?

2. What will you need to make your collage?

3. What can you do with your fall collage?

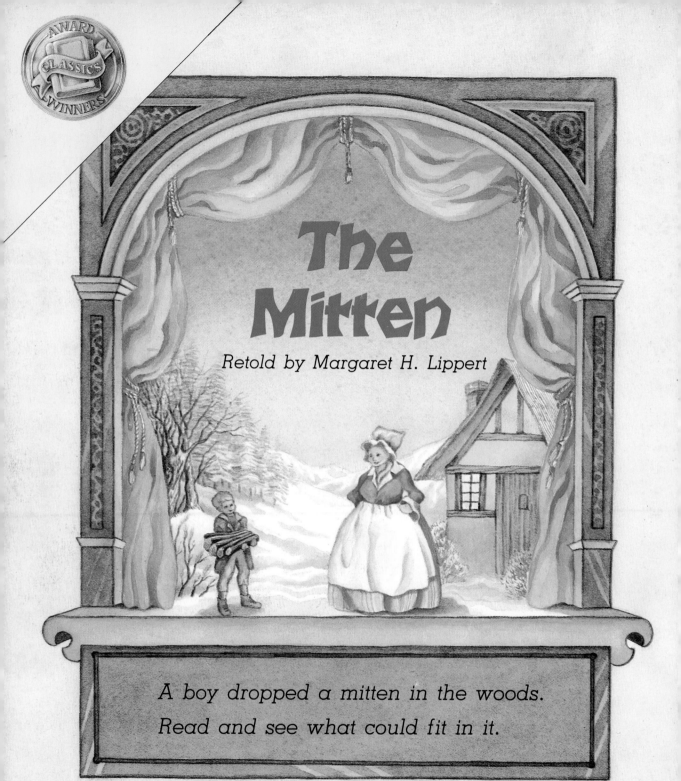

The Mitten

Retold by Margaret H. Lippert

A boy dropped a mitten in the woods.
Read and see what could fit in it.

THE PLAYERS:

 Grandmother

 Boy   **Owl**

 Frog   **Rabbit**

 Mouse   **Bug**

(Boy walks up to Grandmother with wood.)

Boy: I have the wood you asked
me to get, Grandmother, but I
dropped a mitten in the woods.
I will go and look for it now.

Grandmother: No, come in now.
You can't look for your
mitten at night.
You can look for it
another time.

*(Boy and Grandmother
go in.)*

(*Mouse and Frog are in the woods.*)

Frog: What are you looking for, Mouse?

Mouse: I am looking for a new home.

(*She sees the red mitten on the ground.*)

Who dropped that red mitten?
I can live in it.

(*She walks into the mitten.*)

This is my new home!

Frog: May I come in, too?

Mouse: Yes, but don't step on me.

(*Frog hops into the mitten.*)

Frog: I like your new home.

(Owl is in the woods. He sees the mitten.)

Owl: Who dropped that red mitten?

I will fly down and look in it.

Frog: Who is that?

Owl: It is Owl.

May I come in?

Mouse: Yes, you may.

We can all fit.

(Owl walks into the mitten.)

Owl: I like your home.

(Rabbit walks up.)

Rabbit: It is late now.
Where can I sleep?
That mitten will do.

(Rabbit hops up to the mitten.)

Mouse: Who are you?

Rabbit: I am Rabbit.
May I come in?

Owl: Another one can fit.

(Rabbit hops into the mitten.)

Frog: This is fun!

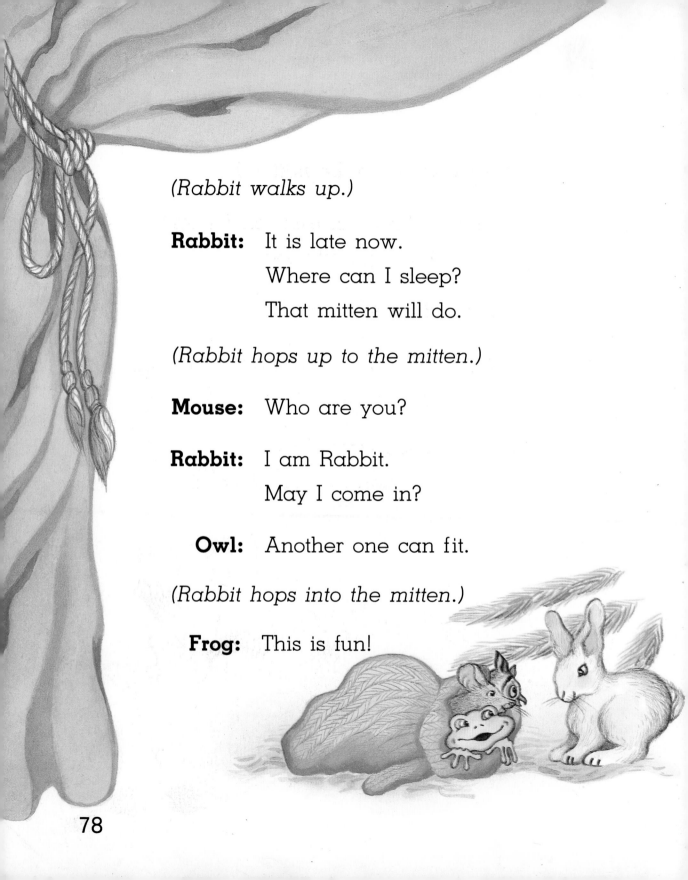

(Bug walks up to the mitten.)

Bug: What is in that red mitten?
I will go and see.

Mouse: STOP! NO MORE!

Frog: We can't fit another
one in this mitten.

Rabbit: Bug is very little.
We can let Bug come in.

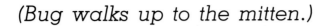

(Bug walks into the mitten. The mitten rips.)

Bug: Look out! Look out!

Frog: Now no one will sleep
in this mitten.

81

(The sun is up. Boy is looking for the mitten.)

Boy: I can't find the mitten
I dropped.

(He sees the mitten on the ground and picks it up.)

Boy: This *was* my mitten.

I will take it home to Grandmother.

She will know what to do with it.

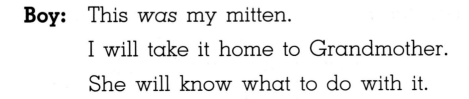

Thinking and Writing About the Selection

1. How did the mitten get in the woods?

2. Who is first to make the mitten a new home?

3. What will Grandmother do with the mitten?

WRITING activity

SENTENCES

Prewrite

In the play, "The Mitten," more and more friends come to live in the little red mitten home. They could not all fit.

Sally Seal likes to ride in a little boat. Friends of Sally like to go, too. The pictures tell the story of Sally. Will all the friends fit in the boat?

1. Sally Seal likes to ride in a little boat to fish.

2. Mark Lion and Amy Rabbit get in the boat to go with Sally.

3. _____ 4. _____

You can write the story of Sally Seal.
Look at the pictures. Pictures 1 and 2
have sentences. You will need to make
up sentences for the next pictures.
What will you say?

Write

1. Write the sentences for
   pictures 1 and 2 on your paper.
2. Write your own sentences for
   pictures 3 and 4 on your paper.

Revise

1. Read your story. Have a friend
   read your story, too.
2. Look at the pictures one more time.
   Did you write sentences for the
   pictures? Do your sentences tell
   the same story as the pictures do?

Make Up Your Own Mind, Billy!

Frank and Jan Asch

The friends could not all fit in
the mitten.
All the things you wish to do may
not fit in a day.
How do you pick what to do?

"Will you come and watch
me swim, Mother?" asked Billy.

"I have to pick up your
grandmother," said Mother.
"Ask your father."

"When can you watch me swim, Dad?"
asked Billy.

"I can go with you now," said Dad.
"You may ask your friends to come,
too, if you like."

Billy and Dad came to the park.

They looked for Don, Sam, and José.

Then Billy said, "Look, Dad!

I see my friends.

They are in that soccer game."

"They are the loudest boys in the park," laughed Dad.

"Billy!" cried Sam.
"Can you play soccer with us?"

"Yes, can you?" cried José.
"We need more players."

"Watch me kick the ball to Billy,"
cried Don, loudest of all.

Billy cried, "Stop!
I can't make up my mind!
I came to ask if you can come
and swim with me.
But I like soccer, too."

89

"I can come if your father
watches us," said Don.

"I like to play soccer," said José.

"Me, too," said Sam.
"Don't quit now, Don!"

"You will have more fun if you play
soccer with us, Billy," said José.
"We can swim another time."

Billy looked at Dad.
"You have to make up your own mind,
Billy," said Dad.

"I know!" said Billy at last.
"We can take a ball with us!"

"I know," said Sam.
"We can play water soccer."

José said, "What is water soccer?
You can't put a soccer ball in water."

Billy said, "I have a ball like
a soccer ball.
We can put it in the water."

"Then I will go," said José.
"When can your father take us?"

"You boys run home and ask if you
can go for a swim," said Dad.
"Then come to the bus stop."

Billy said, "Dad, I could take the red ball, but I like the green one."

Dad looked at Billy.

"I know, I know," Billy laughed. "Make up your own mind, Billy."

Thinking and Writing About the Selection

1. At first, what did Billy wish to do?

2. Where did Billy and Dad find Don, Sam, and José?

3. What did Don, Sam, and Billy wish to do?

Hello and Good-by

Hello and Good-by
Hello and Good-by

When I'm in a swing
Swinging low and then high
Good-by to the ground
Hello to the sky.

Hello to the rain
Good-by to the sun,
Then hello again sun
When the rain is all done

In blows the winter,
Away the birds fly.
Good-by and hello
Hello and good-by

Mary Ann Hoberman

95

Darlene

Eloise Greenfield   *Illustrated by George Ford*

Billy wanted to play one game.

Then he wanted to play another.

Is Darlene like Billy?

Darlene wanted to go back home.

Joanne said, "Come on, we can play."

But Darlene said, "I want to go home!"

Uncle Eddie said, "Your mama will
come to get you at two o'clock."
So Darlene played a game with Joanne.

Then she asked Uncle Eddie,
"Is it two o'clock yet?"

Uncle Eddie said, "Not yet."

So Darlene played another game
with Joanne.
Then she asked Uncle Eddie,
"Is it two o'clock yet?"

Uncle Eddie said, "No, not yet."

So Darlene played one more game
with Joanne.
Then she asked Uncle Eddie,
"Isn't it two o'clock yet?"

But Uncle Eddie said, "Not quite yet."

So Uncle Eddie and
Darlene and Joanne sang songs.
Then Mama was back.
Uncle Eddie said, "Now Darlene,
you can go back home."

Darlene looked at Uncle Eddie.
She looked at Joanne.
She said, "I don't want to go home!"

Uncle Eddie said, "Darlene, you
don't know what you want."

But Darlene said, "Yes, I do.
I want to change my mind when I
want to."

Uncle Eddie laughed.
Joanne and Mama laughed, too.

Then they all sat down and sang songs.
And the one that sang the loudest
was Darlene.

Thinking and Writing About the Selection

1. Who sang songs with Darlene?

2. How did Darlene change?

3. Are Billy and Darlene like
   one another?

New Friends

In this unit, you read about friends who do things with one another.

You read about friends who look for things. They look for shells by the sea, or stars in a night sky.

You saw how friends can have fun when they play games. Friends make things. They can make a collage and a home from a mitten.

Thinking and Writing About *New Friends*

1. In "Make Up Your Own Mind, Billy!" how did Billy make up his mind?

2. What can you do with things you find in the woods or by the sea?

3. How do friends change in "The Giant," and "New Friends for Catfish"?

4. Write a sentence about what you like to find in a friend.

Introducing Level 4

UNDER THE SUN

Each season brings new things to see and do. In this unit, you will read about how things change and grow in each season of the year. What is your favorite season? Why is it your favorite?

**I will be the gladdest thing
   Under the sun!
I will touch a hundred flowers
   And not pick one.**

Edna St. Vincent Millay

Leaves

Argentina Palacios

Red leaves in the fall show change.
Read how Paco will find a friend
in a new home.

Clara likes to make new friends.
One day she spoke to a new boy
in the park.
"My name is Clara," she said.
"What is your name?"

"My name is Paco," said the boy.
He looked at the ground.
"Look at this," he said.
"Red leaves!"

"Are you new in this city?"
asked Clara.

"Yes," said Paco.
"My home was in Puerto Rico, but
now my mother and father and I
live with my grandmother."

"My mother and father had a home in
Puerto Rico, too," said Clara.

Paco looked at the leaves and
said, "In Puerto Rico you don't
see red leaves on the ground and
trees with no leaves at all.
In Puerto Rico the trees are green
all the time."

"The trees had green leaves, but
it is fall now," said Clara.
"In the fall, the leaves change to
red and come down to the ground."

109

"Look!" said Paco.
"That is my mother."

Clara looked and said,
"Your mother is with my mother!
They met when we met!"

"Ask your mother if you can come
to my home," said Paco.
"We can draw.
Do you like to draw?"

"Yes," said Clara.
"I like to trace leaves, too.
We can trace leaves and draw."

"What luck!" thought Paco.
"A new friend."

The next day, Clara came to see Paco.

"Come in," said Paco.

Clara spoke to Mother.

She spoke to Grandmother, too.

Then Paco said to Clara, "We can play now."

Clara said, "We could trace leaves."

So they did.

Then Paco said, "Now we can draw.

I will draw things you can see at an aquarium, like fish and seals."

"I will draw pets," said Clara.

"I will draw a dog, a cat, and a pony."

"Do you want to see my pet?" asked Paco.

"Yes!" said Clara.

"What is it?"

"It is a bird," said Paco.

"What a pretty green bird!"
cried Clara.
"I wish I had a bird like that."

"I had a bird like that when I was
a little girl in Puerto Rico,"
said Grandmother.
"I wish . . ."

"What?" asked Paco.
"What do you wish, Grandmother?"

"I wish for another time,"
said Grandmother.
She looked at the green bird, and
she thought of trees with leaves
that are green all the time.
She thought of Puerto Rico.

Thinking and Writing About the Selection

1. What are the leaves like in
   Puerto Rico?

2. What did Clara and Paco draw?

3. What did Grandmother wish for?

CHANGE

Charlotte Zolotow

The summer
still hangs
heavy and sweet
with sunlight
as it did last year.

The autumn
still comes
showering gold and crimson
as it did last year.

The winter
still stings
clean and cold
and white
as it did last year.

The spring
still comes
like a whisper in the
dark night.

It is only I
who have changed.

Little Robin

Jan Asch

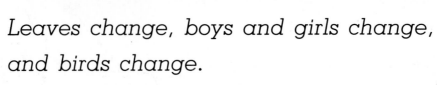

*Leaves change, boys and girls change,
and birds change.
Read how a robin will grow up.*

Little Robin had a home in
a huge tree with Mother Robin and
Father Robin.

One day Father Robin said to Little
Robin, "It is time for you to fly now.
Look at the leaves."
Little Robin could see
red leaves on the ground.

"It is fall," said Father Robin.
"When the moon looks like a huge
ball, every robin will fly to
a new home."

"But Father," said Little Robin,
"I don't want to leave this tree.
This was my first home, and I like it."

"Little Robin," said Father Robin,
"every robin can fly.
I will not let you fall to the ground.
I know you are a brave bird.
I know you can fly, too."

"Father Robin is right," thought
Little Robin.
Then she said, "I know!
I will live in that little birdhouse."

"Who will feed you every day?" asked
Father Robin.

"The man with the birdhouse will
feed me," said Little Robin.

"But do you want to live in a birdhouse?" asked Father Robin.

"It is better to live in a birdhouse than it is to fly," said Little Robin.

"How will you get to the birdhouse if you can't fly?" asked Father Robin.

"I can't fly," said Little Robin, "but I can walk!"

"Flying is better than walking,
Little Robin," said Father Robin.
"This is a huge tree.
How will you get down to the ground?
And when you do get down, how will
you get up to the birdhouse?"

Little Robin did not know how she
could do it.

That night the moon looked like a
huge ball.
Father Robin did not sleep.
He thought and thought.
Little Robin did not sleep.
She thought and thought.

The next day it was time
to leave the huge tree.
Little Robin looked very sad.
Father Robin was not sad.
"If I can help Little Robin fly, she
will come with us," he thought.

"I know how you can get to the
birdhouse," he said to Little Robin.

"How?" asked Little Robin.

"Do what I do," said Father Robin,
and he jumped down to the next branch.
It was not a big jump at all.

"I can do that!" said Little Robin,
and she jumped right down.

"Yes, you can!" said Father Robin,
and he jumped down to the very
next branch.

Little Robin jumped to another and
then another branch.
"With every jump she will get better and
better," thought Father Robin.

Then a branch that Little Robin
jumped on came down with a CRACK!
"I will fall to the ground!" cried
Little Robin.

But she was brave, and she jumped up.
"I can fly!" she cried.
"You are right, Father!
Flying is better than walking!"

"Now you can fly to the birdhouse,"
said Father Robin.

"No, I don't need to go to the
birdhouse now," said Little Robin.
"I want to fly with you and Mother and
all my friends.
It is better to fly with friends
than to live in a birdhouse!"

Thinking and Writing About the Selection

1. Where could Little Robin
    live when all the birds leave
    the tree?

2. How did Father Robin get
    Little Robin to fly?

3. How did Little Robin grow up?

WRITING
activity

DIRECTIONS

Prewrite

Father Robin wanted to help Little Robin to fly. So he had Little Robin do what he did, one step at a time, and she did fly.

Look at this picture. Turtle is looking for home, but he can't find it. You can write sentences that will help Turtle. You will need to write one step at a time. Then Turtle can read what you say and get home.

Turtle's home

Write

1. Write the first two sentences.
2. Now write sentences of your own.
   Your sentences may look like this.

Turtle, you are at the clock in the park.
First go down to the big red tree.
Now _____
Then _____
Next _____
Last _____

Revise

1. Read your sentences. Let a friend
   read your sentences, too.
2. Do your sentences tell Turtle how to
   get home one step at a time? If not,
   what more can you tell Turtle?

SNOWBALL

Susan J. Shillcock and Kathleen Johnson Dohn

The change in leaves shows a little
robin that it is time to fly.
Now read and find out what a rabbit
will do in the first snow.

"Come to me, Snowball!" Jerry said
to his new pet rabbit.

"Look how Snowball hops to you, Jerry,"
laughed his mother.
"She looks like a big snowball,
doesn't she?"

"I want Snowball to see snow,"
said Jerry.
"When will it snow?"

"Now that it is winter,
I know it *will* snow, Jerry, but I
don't know *when*," said his mother.

Jerry sang, "I hope it will snow.
I hope it will snow.
I hope, I hope, I hope it will snow!"

That night, when it was time to go
to sleep, Jerry asked, "May I go out
and see Snowball first?"

"You may," said his father,
"but come right back in."

Jerry ran out to see Snowball, but
he was back in no time at all.
"I can't find Snowball!" cried Jerry
to his mother and father.

"We can't go and look for your
rabbit now, Jerry," said his father.
"It is too late.
The rabbit will do all right
for one night."

"But what if it snows?" asked Jerry.
"Where will Snowball go?
Where will she sleep?"

"Snowball will do all right, Jerry,"
said his father.

135

Jerry sat in the big chair and thought
of Snowball.

"I hope it doesn't snow," he thought.

"I hope it doesn't snow.

I hope, I hope, I hope it doesn't snow."

The next day Jerry was up
at first light.

"Wake up, Dad!" he said to his father.

"Look!

It did snow!"

"I looked for Snowball last night,
Jerry," said his father, "but I had no luck.
We can look now if you like."

"Yes, yes!" cried Jerry.

In no time, the family was out looking
for the little rabbit.
They looked and looked, but they
did not find Snowball.

"We may not find your rabbit, Jerry,"
said his father.
"We may not see a rabbit that looks
like snow in the snow."

Then Jerry cried,
"Look! Rabbit tracks!
I will go where the tracks go!"
He ran quickly to where he could
see more tracks.
At last he did find Snowball,
right next to the big tree!

139

Jerry picked up his rabbit.

"Snowball, what were you doing?"
he asked.

"Were you playing a trick on us?"

"Look, Jerry!" cried his mother.

Jerry looked down.

"Now I see what you were doing, Snowball," he laughed.

"You are the pet in my family, but now you have a family of your own!"

Thinking and Writing About the Selection

1. When did Jerry find out that Snowball was not at home?

2. How did Father and Jerry find Snowball?

3. What did Snowball have out in the snow?

141

A Winter Day

Kathleen Johnson Dohn

On a winter day, it may take time
to find a rabbit that looks like snow.
But it will take no time at all to
find Ben.

Ben wakes up and hops out of bed.
Is there anything to do on this
winter day?
He looks outside.
The first snow of the winter came
last night!
There is snow on the ground and on
the trees.
There is snow on the car.
What a good day it is to play outside!

Ben finds his sled.
He is the first one outside.
The snow is so pretty!
Ben plays that he is flying on the
snow with his sled.

Then Amy and Mother come out.
Amy sees snow for the first time.
She laughs and laughs.
Ben likes to push the sled for Amy.

"Look, Mother!" says Ben.
"I will make a bird in the snow."

"That is a good bird," says Mother,
"but can you make a mouse?"

Ben laughs and says, "That is a good
mouse, but can you make a turtle?"

Mother laughs and says, "I can make
anything you can make!
It is fun to play in the snow."

145

Dad is the last one to come outside.

"Come to the park with me," he says.

"What will we do there?" says Ben.

"There is ice on the lake," says Dad,
"so you know what I will do!
I will skate.
You can skate with me.
You can play with your sled.
You can play tag.
You can do anything you like."

Is there anything fun to do in the
winter?
Ben and Amy say, "Yes!"
Mother and Dad say, "Yes!"
What do you say?

Thinking and Writing About the Selection

1. What did Ben do first
   out in the snow?

2. How did Ben make things in
   the snow?

3. What do you like to do in the snow?

RECALL DETAILS

A. Read the story. Then read the questions.
Write the answers on your paper.

A Bird Looks for a Home

A red bird was looking for a home.
It looked in a hat, but the hat was too little.
It looked in the sea, but it did not
know how to swim.
At last it looked in a tree.
There was a birdhouse!
A boy and girl had made it.
The bird had a new home.

1. Who was looking for a home?
2. Why couldn't the hat be a
   birdhouse?
3. Did the bird know how to swim?
4. Who had made the birdhouse?

148

B. Read the story.

Answer the questions on your paper.

A Winter Day

Last night was the first snow.

Ben runs outside to play on his sled.

Then Mother and Amy come out.

Ben makes a bird in the snow,

and his mother makes a mouse.

Dad is the last one outside.

Now the family can go to the park.

In the park, they can skate,

play tag, make things in the

snow, or do anything they like.

1. What was last night?
2. Who made a mouse
   in the snow?
3. Who came outside last?
4. What can the family do at the park?

Squirrel and the Pine Nuts

Retold by Margaret H. Lippert

Leaves fall to the ground
in the fall and so do pine nuts.
Read and find out what a squirrel
will do with pine nut seeds.

It was fall, and Tikkuntsih, the red
squirrel, was looking for pine nuts
in the woods.

There were leaves on the ground, but
Tikkuntsih did not want leaves.

There were flowers, too, but he did
not like flowers.

"I do not want leaves and flowers,"
Tikkuntsih thought.

"I want pine nuts.

I do like pine nuts."

At the same time two boys, Gray Owl
and Little Fox, were looking in
the same woods for pine nuts.
They had to find pine nuts to
take home.
They had good luck.
They did find pine nuts, and they
put the pine nuts into a bag.
Then they sat down on a big rock.
"Now we have time to play,"
Gray Owl said.

"First, I want to have a pine nut,"
said Little Fox.

"No," said Gray Owl.
"We can't have the pine nuts now.
They are to take home.
You know that."

"It will not matter if we have just
one," said Little Fox.
"No one will know."

"It will matter to us,"
said Gray Owl.
"We will know.
Now hide the bag next
to the rock so we can play.
We have just a little time."
Little Fox put the bag down
and ran to play.

Now all this time Tikkuntsih was
looking at the boys.
He had seen where Little Fox
put the bag.
The boys had not seen Tikkuntsih.
When they were playing, Tikkuntsih
ran to the rock and picked up the
bag of pine nuts.
Then he ran up a tree with the bag.

Just then, the boys came back.
Little Fox looked next to the rock
where he had put the bag, but
nothing was there.
"Come quickly!" he said to Gray Owl.

"What is the matter?"
asked Gray Owl.

"Look!" said Little Fox.
"I put the bag down right next to that
rock, but now there is nothing there!"
The boys looked and looked for the
bag of pine nuts.

When night came and they had seen
nothing on the ground, they had to
stop looking and go home.
But Tikkuntsih was in luck.
He had all the pine nuts he wanted.

Tikkuntsih ran home with the bag
of pine nuts.

Every now and then he sat down
on a big rock and had a pine nut,
and every time he had one,
he dropped another one on the ground.

The pine nut seeds Tikkuntsih dropped
were in the ground all winter.

When spring came, the sun helped the
pine nut seeds push up out of the
ground and grow.

Now the little pine nuts are big
pine nut trees, and there is a
pine nut tree next to every
big rock in the woods.

Thinking and Writing About the Selection

1. Who wanted pine nuts?

2. How did Tikkuntsih get the
   pine nuts?

3. How did pine nut trees come
   to grow next to every big
   rock in the woods?

At the Edge

At the edge of the world
It is growing light.
The trees stand shining.
I like it.
It is growing light.

Papago

of the World

A DESERT ANIMAL

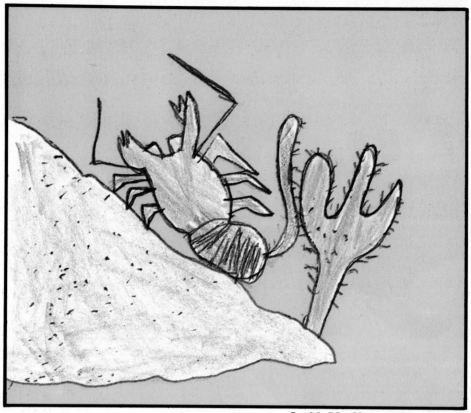

Jeff Hall, age seven

Pine nut trees grow in woods
next to the desert.
In the desert, there is a
night animal you may not know.

This animal is a vinegarroon.

It lives in the desert.

The vinegarroon likes the night.

The days in the desert are too hot.

The vinegarroon can get under a rock.

It may hide under the rock all day.

Vinegarroons have eight legs.
They have eight eyes, too.
They need eight eyes to watch
out for owls and snakes!
Vinegarroons don't like owls and
big snakes.

The vinegarroon can play a trick
on another animal.
The vinegarroon can make a smell.
The animal will not like the smell.
The smell is like vinegar.
That is how the vinegarroon got
its name.

Thinking and Writing About the Selection

1. What is a vinegarroon?

2. What do vinegarroons look like?

 3. How did the vinegarroon get
its name?

SKILLS activity

CONTEXT CLUES

Look at the word in the box.

Think what the word in the box means.

Write each sentence on your paper.

A vinegarroon has eight legs.

A vinegarroon likes to get under a rock.

1. A vinegarroon is a _____.

   desert animal

   pine tree

A vinegarroon is a desert animal.

You can see footprints in the sand.

An animal leaves footprints.

2. Footprints are _____.

   tracks

   boats

A cactus is green.

A cactus grows in the desert.

3. A cactus is a _____.

city

plant

An ocean has fish in it.

An ocean is very big.

4. An ocean is a _____.

house

big sea

A chipmunk is like a squirrel.

A chipmunk lives in the woods.

5. A chipmunk is an _____.

animal

aquarium

The Wind and the Sun

Retold by Margaret H. Lippert

In the desert, the sun is very hot.

Is the sun stronger than the wind?

Read and see.

One day the Wind said to the Sun,
"I am stronger than you are."

"Don't brag," said the Sun.
"We will see who is stronger.
There is a man walking home.
I can make that man take his coat off.
Can you?"

"Yes, I can," said the Wind.

"Then you go first," said the Sun.

"I will show you what I can do,"
said the Wind.

The Wind blew and blew.
The man looked up at the sky.
"This is like winter," he said.
"I need this good coat."

The man did not take off his coat.
The Wind couldn't win.
The Sun laughed at the Wind.

"Now," said the Sun, "we will see
who is stronger.
I will make that man take off
his coat."

"What a joke," said the Wind.
"I couldn't make the man take off
his coat.
I know you can't do it.
You are too little.
I am very big."

"Look at me," said the Sun.

The Sun came out.
The man sat down.
"I am very hot," he said.
"This is like summer.
I can't keep this coat on."
He put his coat down on the ground.

The Sun said, "I win.
When I come out it gets hot.
The man got too hot.
He got so hot that he had to take
off his coat, so I am stronger
than you."

Thinking and Writing About the Selection

1. When the Wind and the Sun first talk, who says it is the stronger of the two?

2. How did the Sun win?

3. How did the Wind brag?

Robert Kraus

Leo the Late Bloomer

Illustrated by José Aruego

Fall, winter, spring, and summer
. . . change will come with time.
Will change come for Leo?
Read and find out.

Leo couldn't do anything right.

He couldn't read.

He couldn't write.

He couldn't draw.

He was a sloppy eater.

And, he never said a word.

owl

Elephant

Snake

Plover

Crocodile

"What's the matter with Leo?"
asked Leo's father.

"Nothing," said Leo's mother.
"Leo is just a late bloomer."

"Better late than never," thought
Leo's father.

Every day Leo's father watched him for signs of blooming.
And every night Leo's father watched him for signs of blooming.

178

"Are you sure Leo's a bloomer?"
asked Leo's father.

"Patience," said Leo's mother.
"A watched bloomer doesn't bloom."

So Leo's father watched television
instead of Leo.

The snows came.
Leo's father wasn't watching.
But Leo still wasn't blooming.

The trees budded.

Leo's father wasn't watching.

But Leo still wasn't blooming.

181

Then one day, in his own good time,
Leo bloomed!
He could read!
He could write!
He could draw!
He ate neatly!

He also spoke.

And it wasn't just a word.

It was a whole sentence.

And that sentence was . . .

"I made it!"

**Thinking and Writing
About the Selection**

1. For what did Leo's father watch?

2. When Leo bloomed, what could
   he do at last?

3. What made Leo a late bloomer?

183

Robert Kraus

Robert Kraus was ten years old when he sold a funny sign to the local barber. When he was eleven he had a cartoon published.

Kraus always loved to draw. "I read books about how to become a cartoonist." These books told him how to draw funny signs and sell them.

When Kraus grew up, he became a cartoonist for magazines. Putting cartoons together was like writing a book. Today Robert Kraus writes books because "it's nice to communicate with children."

More to Read   *Noel the Coward*
Whose Mouse Are You?
Milton the Early Riser

WORDS FOR THE SEASONS

| Summer | Winter | Spring | Fall |

Answer these riddles about the four seasons.

1. When you skate on the ice and sled on the snow, it is _____.

2. When the red leaves fall down and school begins, it is _____.

3. When it is hot and you can swim and find shells, it is _____.

4. When the birds sing and flowers bloom and everything turns green, it is _____.

5. Think of season words. Write a riddle.

THE GUEST

Arnold Lobel

Owl was at home.

"How good it feels to be sitting
by this fire," said Owl.

"It is so cold and snowy outside."

Owl was eating buttered toast
and hot pea soup for supper.

Owl heard a loud sound
at the front door.
"Who is out there, banging and
pounding at my door on a night
like this?" he said.
Owl opened the door.
No one was there.
Only the snow and the wind.

Owl sat near the fire again.
There was another loud noise
at the door.
"Who can it be," said Owl,
"knocking and thumping
at my door on a night like this?"
Owl opened the door.

No one was there.

Only the snow and the cold.

"The poor old winter is knocking
at my door," said Owl.

"Perhaps it wants to sit
by the fire.

Well, I will be kind
and let the winter come in."

Owl opened his door very wide.

"Come in, Winter," said Owl.

"Come in and warm yourself

for a while."

Winter came into the house.
It came in very fast.
A cold wind
pushed Owl against the wall.

Winter ran around the room.
It blew out the fire
in the fireplace.

The snow whirled up the stairs
and whooshed down the hallway.
"Winter!" cried Owl.
"You are my guest.
This is no way to behave!"
But Winter did not listen.

It made the window shades
flap and shiver.
It turned the pea soup
into hard, green ice.

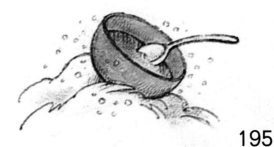

Winter went into all the rooms
of Owl's house.
Soon everything was covered
with snow.
"You must go, Winter!" shouted Owl.
"Go away, right now!"

The wind blew around and around.
Then Winter rushed out and
slammed the front door.
"Good-bye," called Owl, "and do
not come back!"

Owl made a new fire
in the fireplace.
The room became warm again.
The snow melted away.
The hard, green ice turned back
into soft pea soup.
Owl sat down in his
chair and quietly finished his supper.

Under the Sun

In this unit, you read about things that change and grow.

You saw that first times and new things come with the change of seasons.

You saw change come quickly, and by surprise, when a rabbit has a new family.

You saw change take more time, as it did with Leo the late bloomer.

Thinking and Writing About *Under the Sun*

1. What are vinegarroons and where do they live?

2. In "Snowball," Ben said at first, "I hope it will snow." Why did he change his mind?

3. How is Little Robin like Leo?

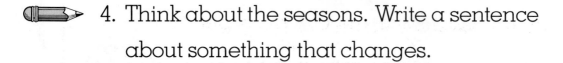 4. Think about the seasons. Write a sentence about something that changes.

Picture Dictionary

A a

all
All the boys have books.

animal
Not every animal will make a good pet.

another
One book is in the bag.
Another is on the step.

anything
Is there anything in the bag?

aquarium
You can see fish, sea lions,
and seals at the aquarium.

are
Do you know who we are?

asked
Jill asked Dad if she could have a pet.

B b

ball

Watch the dog run for the <u>ball</u>!

better

"This chair looks <u>better</u>," said Tim.

birdhouse

What lives in the <u>birdhouse</u>?

blew

The wind <u>blew</u> the hat.

bloom

In spring, the flowers <u>bloom</u> and look pretty.

bloomer

Look at the flowers. One is a late <u>bloomer</u>.

branch

The birds sit on a <u>branch</u> of the tree.

B b

brave
The diver is a <u>brave</u> man!

C c

catfish
A <u>catfish</u> is a fish that looks like a cat.

chair
"Sit in this <u>chair</u>," said Mark.

change
Ted will <u>change</u> his things.

coat
Jenny has a new red <u>coat</u>.

collage
Don makes a <u>collage</u> out of wood, shells, and seeds.

couldn't
No matter where he looked, Leo <u>couldn't</u> find his hat.

C c

cried
Eddie was so sad that he <u>cried</u>.

D d

desert
Very little can grow in a <u>desert</u>.

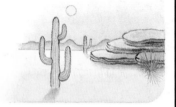

diver
The <u>diver</u> will go into the water.

dives
The bird <u>dives</u> for the fish.

doesn't
It <u>doesn't</u> snow in the summer.

don't
<u>Don't</u> walk when the light is red.

draw
Leo and Greg <u>draw</u> a bird and a birdhouse.

D d

dropped

Nan <u>dropped</u> the ball on the ground.

E e

eight

I can see <u>eight</u> stars in the sky.

every

<u>Every</u> car is green.

eyes

You have two <u>eyes</u> to see with.

F f

fall

In the <u>fall</u>, the woods look red.

family

This <u>family</u> is watching a show.

F f

father

Father shows Darlene how to fish.

feed

Carlos will feed the dog.

find

"Can you help me find
my mitten?" asked Tom.

first

If Amy walks more quickly than Anna,
she will get home first.

flowers

These plants have flowers.

fox

A fox is an animal that looks like a little dog.

friend

I like Pam. She is my friend.

G g

glue

Jim will <u>glue</u> shells and wood to the collage.

good

Ned and his family like to have <u>good</u> things to eat.

gray

This animal is <u>gray</u>.

ground

Plants grow in the <u>ground</u>.

gym

We play ball in the <u>gym</u>.

H h

have

Jeff and Nan <u>have</u> two cats, a bird, and a dog.

his

Don looks at <u>his</u> tracks.

H h

hope

I hope the branch doesn't crack with the bird on it.

how

How will the map help Amy find the park?

huge

The dog looks huge next to the little fish.

I i

into

The woman put the new books into the bag.

isn't

The girl isn't happy.

J j

just

Just one animal is a bird.

L l

last
Who came in <u>last</u>?

laughed
Pam <u>laughed</u> at the trick the man did.

leave
Father and Jane <u>leave</u> the boat.

leaves
The <u>leaves</u> are on the ground.

loudest
Pam sang the <u>loudest</u> of all the girls.

M m

mama
The little girl said, "<u>Mama</u>, take me with you."

matter
When the baby cried, what was the <u>matter</u>?

M m

mind

"I can't make up <u>mind</u>," said Tami.

mitten

One <u>mitten</u> is green, and one is red.

more

Mary sees <u>more</u> shells.

mouse

The cat is looking at the little <u>mouse</u>.

N n

name

My <u>name</u> is Linda.

need

We <u>need</u> to sleep at night.

never

These plants will <u>never</u> grow if they don't get water.

N n

new

"Look at my <u>new</u> hat!"

next

She has seen all the pets. <u>Next</u>, she will pick one.

no

"<u>No</u>, Buster!" cried Tom. "Down!"

nothing

He will have <u>nothing</u> to eat if you do not feed him.

O o

o'clock

At six <u>o'clock</u> it is time to go home.

of

Scott looks at a map <u>of</u> the park.

off

The wind blew <u>off</u> her hat.

O o

one
One apple is green.

outside
Jeff and Greg like to play outside in the woods.

owl
An owl is a bird that likes the night.

own
With your own clock, you can get up when you wish.

P p

plants
The seeds will grow into plants.

players
Here are the players in a play.

pods
What is in the pods?

P p

pretty

Kate looks <u>pretty</u> in her new coat.

Puerto Rico

Can you find <u>Puerto</u> <u>Rico</u> on the map?

R r

rabbit

The little <u>rabbit</u> hops to its home in the woods.

right

Is Leo doing what is <u>right</u>?

robin

A <u>robin</u> is a little red bird.

S s

said

Mother <u>said</u>, "You may ride the pony."

S s

sang

Jim <u>sang</u> at home.

say

What do you <u>say</u> if you are asked, "How are you?"

sea lions

<u>Sea lions</u> look like seals.

seal

The <u>seal</u> likes fish.

seen

Leo has <u>seen</u> that the boat is big and red.

sentence

Tami can write a <u>sentence</u>.

sharks

<u>Sharks</u> are big fish.

shells

We look for pretty <u>shells</u> in the sea.

S s

signs

What are the <u>signs</u> of spring?

skate

In winter, Scott and
Paco <u>skate</u> on the ice.

sled

It is fun to take a <u>sled</u> out in the snow.

smell

The cat likes the
<u>smell</u> of the flowers.

snakes

<u>Snakes</u> can live in the desert or the woods.

snow

I want to play in the winter <u>snow</u>.

snowball

Tami made a <u>snowball</u>.

S s

so

"Get into the car," said Mother, "<u>so</u> we can go."

soccer

The boys will play <u>soccer</u> with that ball.

songs

Anna and Tim sang <u>songs</u> at home.

spoke

The man <u>spoke</u> to Mary and Paco.

spring

Trees get new leaves in the <u>spring</u>.

squirrel

A <u>squirrel</u> is a little animal that likes to eat nuts.

stars

We saw the <u>stars</u> in the night sky.

stronger

Darlene is <u>stronger</u> than Jim.

S s

summer

In <u>summer</u> the sun is hot.

T t

than

Father will eat more <u>than</u> Tim.

then

First Tim sees Meg, and
<u>then</u> he sees the rabbit.

there

"<u>There</u> is no bird in the tree.
But look <u>there</u>, on the ground."

they

Jan and Ned like the water. <u>They</u> like to swim.

things

What <u>things</u> are in the bag?

T t

thought

Jenny sat and <u>thought</u> about winter.

trees

<u>Trees</u> can have pretty red leaves in the fall.

turtle

This <u>turtle</u> lives in the woods.

two

<u>Two</u> boys push the car.

U u

under

A bug can hide <u>under</u> a rock.

V v

vinegar

Tami doesn't like the smell of <u>vinegar</u>.

V v

vinegarroon

A <u>vinegarroon</u> has eight legs and lives in the desert.

W w

want

Do you <u>want</u> my book?

was

Jan <u>was</u> on the bus, but now she is home.

watch

Jim and Joanne <u>watch</u> the play.

were

A bird and a cat <u>were</u> in the snow.

when

<u>When</u> will the bus come?

who

"<u>Who</u> can read the time?" asked Father.

W w

wind

The <u>wind</u> blew and picked up the leaves.

winter

Do you like to skate or ride on a sled in the <u>winter</u>?

wood

Father and Jill pick up <u>wood</u>.

word

Can you read the <u>word</u> *birdhouse*?

write

Carlos can <u>write</u> his name.

Y y

yes

Ben says, "<u>Yes</u>, you may take a giant step."

your

"May I see <u>your</u> map?" Tim asked Amy.

Word List

To the teacher: The following words are introduced in *Taking Time*. The page number to the left of a word indicates where the word first appears in the selection.

Instructional-Vocabulary Words are printed in black. Words printed in red are Applied-Skills Words that children should be able to decode independently, using previously taught phonics skills. Story Words are printed in blue. These are proper names and content area words that children need to be familiar with to read a particular selection.

Unit 1: New Friends

A New Friend
10. new
    friend
11. was
    ran
    said
    gym
12. girl
    sad
13. mat
14. name

The Giant
16. they
17. don't
    run
    tag
18. stars
    mad
    are
    fun
    brave
20. us
21. yes
    giants

Skills Activity
27. first
    last
    next
    then

Buster and the Fish
29. who
29. asked
30. came
    your
    one
    aquarium
31. plants
    six
    same
32. feed
    sat
34. an

At the Aquarium
41. isn't
    of
    seals
    turtles

42. map
all
shows
more
sea lions
43. diver
dives
46. sharks

**New Friends
for Catfish**
48. Catfish
Seal
Turtle
friends
50. let
no
laughed
51. am
own
53. mine
change
54. cried

Shells Don't Walk
58. if
shells

58. tide
59. day
so
pretty
60. things
make
find
61. hat
bits
wood
63. hide
had
rock
trick

A Collage
69. woods
collage
ground
how
need
fall
pods
nuts
70. have
72. glue

The Mitten
74. dropped
mitten
fit
75. players
Owl
boy
Rabbit
Frog
Bug
Mouse
another
76. looking
into
hops
78. late
80. rips

**Make Up Your
Own Mind, Billy!**
87. watch
ask
father
when
Dad
88. looked

88. soccer
    game
    loudest
89. kick
    ball
    mind
90. watches
    quit

Darlene

96. wanted
97. want
98. Mama
    two
    o'clock
    played
    yet
100. quite
101. sang
    songs
    back

Unit 2: Under the Sun

Leaves

106. leaves
107. spoke
108. Puerto Rico
109. trees
110. met
111. draw
    trace
    luck
    thought

Little Robin

118. birds
    Robin
119. huge
    tree
120. every
    leave
122. right
    birdhouse
123. better

123. than
125. flying
    walking
127. jumped
    branch
128. crack

Snowball

132. snow
133. Snowball
    his
    doesn't
    winter
    hope
135. snows
136. chair
137. wake
138. family
139. tracks
140. picked
    were
    doing
    playing

This part of *Taking Time* is a review of letters and the sounds they stand for. Looking carefully at these letters will help you know how to say and read many new words.

Lessons

1. Initial Consonants
2. Initial Consonants
3. Initial Consonants
4. Final Consonants
5. Short Vowels and Graphemic Bases
6. Short Vowels and Graphemic Bases
7. Short Vowels and Graphemic Bases

1 Initial Consonants

A. Say the animal names.

Listen for the sound you hear at the beginning of the name.

Write the letter that stands for that sound on your paper.

1. n c m

2. n p k

3. m p l

4. b p h

5. p b h

6. m n c

B. Find the word that fits in the sentence.
Write the sentence with the word.

1. Is that pony your ____?   pet   met

2. Can it ride in the ____?   bar   car

3. No, it can ____.   hot   not

4. It is too ____ for that.   big   pig

5. But we can ride ____ pony!   my   by

6. We can get ____ for it.   hay   may

7. We can be ____ to it.   mind   kind

8. The pony will ____ that!   hike   like

2 Initial Consonants

A. Look at the letters in the box.
Find the letters that make the
words go with the pictures.
Write the words on your paper.

c	g	s	t	w	z

Where I Like to Go

1. the __ity

2. the __oods

3. the __oo

4. the __ea

5. the __ame

6. the __op

B. Find the letter that makes each word. Write each sentence on your paper.

What I Like to Do

1. I play __ag.   c   t   v

2. I ride in a __an.   g   s   v

3. I make a __ish.   c   w   z

4. I see a __ood   c   g   s
   ball __ame.   g   v   z

5. I look at a __eal   f   s   w
   in the __ity   c   f   z
   __oo.   s   w   z

6. I have __un   f   t   v
   with my __amily.   g   f   t

3 Initial Consonants

A. Find the letters that make

the words that name the pictures.

Now write the words on your paper.

Then write the sentences.

d	g	j	r

1. He is a ___iant.

2. He ___ives

off the ___ock.

3. He ___eads

on a ___ock.

4. He has a ___abbit

for his pet.

5. He has no car.

He has a ___et.

B. Read each sentence.
Find the letter or letters that
make a word to fit the sentence.
Write the sentences on your paper.

1. The giant and the __abbit
wanted to swim.

| r | d | qu |

2. "__ump in!" said the giant.

| Y | J | Qu |

3. "I __ust can't," said the rabbit.

| y | qu | j |

4. "I can't go in __et."

| d | r | y |

5. "We can __it and go home,"
said the giant.

| qu | r | j |

6. Then they saw a __uck.

| g | j | d |

7. "Are __ou and I as brave

| j | y | g |

8. as she is?" asked the rabbit.
"__es!" the giant said.

| D | R | Y |

9. The rabbit and the giant
__umped right in!

| d | y | j |

231

4 Final Consonants

Look at the picture.

Choose the ending that makes a rhyme.

Write the rhyme on your paper.

1. There is a goa___
in the boa___. | n | t |

2. Can a fro___
ride on a do___? | m | g |

3. This boo___
can coo___! | k | t |

4. Why does the ma___
run on a ca___? | n | ck |

5. This is a pet
I want to kee___.
I will take it to bed
when I go to slee___. | d | p |

6. I have a fish.
I call it Ti___.
It can not hop,
but it can swi___. | p | m |

7. Fat and funny
Mr. Qua___
has a sna___ pa___
on his ba___. | ck | g |

233

5 Short Vowels and Graphemic Bases

A. What letters make a word that
can go in each sentence?
Write each sentence on your paper.

an	at	ad	ag

1. A c___ is a good pet.

2. Friends can run and play t___.

3. This is not good. It is b___.

4. A father is a m___.

5. We can put things in a b___.

6. She doesn't laugh. She is s___.

7. I s___ in the chair.

8. The dog did not sit. It r___!

B. Read each story. Read the words in the box.

Find one word that answers the question.

Write it on your paper.

1. You can walk on this.

A cat may sleep on it.

What is it?

man
mat
mad

2. I am a girl.

I like to play a game.

I can run and run when I play.

What game is it?

tag
tug
tan

3. There is snow outside.

I want to go out.

I will put this on.

What do I put on?

had
hot
hat

4. My friend is not home.

I have no one to play with.

How do I feel?

sad
sat
sag

6 Short Vowels and Graphemic Bases

Look at the picture.

Choose the ending that makes a rhyme.

Write the rhyme on your paper.

1. A cat with a f___

in a b___ | ock | ox |

2. A frog on a r___

with just one s___ | ock | op |

3. The things in the p___

got very h___ | et | ot |

4. A rabbit who can h___
and m___   `ox` `op`

5. T___ m___
walking a h___   `ed` `en`

6. A p___
who wanted a j___   `ed` `et`

word work

7 Short Vowels and Graphemic Bases

A. Find the letters that make the picture word.

Write the word on your paper.

1. b _____
   - ip
   - ick
   - ug

2. d _____
   - ock
   - uck
   - un

3. s _____
   - un
   - ip
   - im

4. sh _____
   - ip
   - up
   - ug

5. h _____
   - um
   - it
   - ug

6. p _____
   - up
   - um
   - ip

B. Find the letters that make each word.
Write the sentences on your paper.

| ug | um | un | up | uck |

1. Tim is a b___.

2. He can sit on a c___.

3. With a little l___, he will not fall in.

4. But if Tim falls, he can dry in the s___.

5. He will swim and play,

and a song he will h___.

| im | ip | it | ick |

1. Kim the mouse tried

to s___ like Tim.

2. She went to the cup and

jumped on the r___.

3. When Kim went down, she was qu___ to see

a mouse can't f___ on a cup of tea.